advance music | play-along

Jim Snidero

Easy Jazz Conception
Alto Saxophone

**15 solo etudes
for jazz phrasing,
interpretation
and improvisation**
played by
Jim Snidero

includes online audio material

ADV 14760
ISMN 979-2063-0420-0
ISBN 978-3-89221-195-2

advance music

www.advancemusic.com | © 1999/2020 advance music GmbH, Mainz | Printed in Germany

Cover image: 10eg Visual

Cover design: Elke Dörr

Music engraving: Walter Gruber

German translation: Paul Müller

Text editors: Don & Diane Erjavec, Claudia Gruber

Production: Hans Gruber

Special thanks to Hans Gruber for his encouragement and support,

to my wife Myoung Shin for her patience and support, to my father,

and to Slide Hampton, Eric Alexander, Ryan Kisor, Joe Cohn,

Mike LeDonne, Peter Washington, and Kenny Washington.

TABLE OF CONTENTS

 Please visit www.schott-music.com/online-material to download all audio files for free using the following voucher code:

JCjsAB99

Auf der Website www.schott-music.com/online-material können alle Audio-Dateien mit dem folgenden Gutscheincode kostenlos heruntergeladen werden:

JCjsAB99

Musicians on the recording:
Jim Snidero – Alto Saxophone
Mike LeDonne – Piano
Peter Washington – Bass
Kenny Washington – Drums
Recorded at Acoustic Recording
Engineer – Michael Brorby
Producer – Jim Snidero
Executive producer – Hans Gruber

Jim Snidero

Kenny Washington

Mike LeDonne

Peter Washington

Jim Snidero (© Heike Rost)
Kenny Washington, Mike LeDonne, Peter Washington (© Ken Franckling)

INTRODUCTION

One of the most important aspects of playing any style of music well is to interpret it in an idiomatically correct way. In jazz, knowing how to phrase common melodies and rhythms, swinging and developing a good tone are all essential elements in sounding both convincing and authentic. **Easy Jazz Conception** is a collection of 15 solo etudes based on standard chord progressions and blues that is intended to give musicians, unfamiliar with the jazz idiom, a basic proficiency in jazz style.

To aid in the study of phrasing, the first ten etudes have many of the phrasings indicated with *tenuto* (–) and *marcato* (ʌ) markings. It's difficult to indicate on the written page exactly how long or short something is played, but in general a *marcato* (ʌ) should be played fairly short but with some weight. The end of an eighth-note phrase is almost always short.

Einer der wichtigsten Aspekte, wenn Sie einen Musikstil gut spielen wollen, ist ihn idiomatisch richtig zu interpretieren. Auf den Jazz übertragen bedeutet dies die Fähigkeit, gängige Melodiefiguren und Rhythmen richtig zu phrasieren, zu swingen und einen guten Ton zu entwickeln. Alle diese Elemente tragen dazu bei, überzeugend und authentisch zu klingen. **Easy Jazz Conception** ist eine Sammlung von 15 Soloetüden, die auf Standard- und Bluesformen basieren. Die Reihe zielt darauf ab, Musikern, die mit dem Jazzidiom nicht vertraut sind, fundamentale Kenntnisse in der Jazzstilistik zu vermitteln.

In den ersten zehn Etüden sind zur Erleichterung die meisten *Tenuto* (–) und *Marcato* (ʌ) Phrasierungszeichen notiert. *Marcato* bedeutet, dass eine Note ziemlich kurz, aber mit einer gewissen Betonung gespielt wird. Die letzte Note einer Achtelphrase wird meist immer kurz gespielt.

The last five etudes are more typical looking charts with limited phrasings indicated. At this point, you should be able to better interpret the etude without every phrase being indicated. If you're not sure how something is phrased, refer to the recording. Ultimately, you have to listen to the recording and emulate the way the soloist phrases.

Die letzten fünf Etüden sind, wie typische Jazz Charts, nur mit wenigen Phrasierungszeichen versehen. Sie sollten nun in der Lage sein, die Etüden ohne solche Zeichen richtig zu interpretieren. Hören Sie sich die Aufnahme an, wenn Sie nicht sicher sind, wie eine bestimmte Phrase interpretiert werden soll. Hören Sie sich letztlich immer die Aufnahme an und versuchen Sie, die Phrasierung des Solisten genau zu kopieren.

Individual Use for Easy Jazz Conception

Easy Jazz Conception Serie im Einzelunterricht

There are two tracks on the recording for each etude. One track has the soloist playing the etude with the rhythm section (soloist/rhythm section track) and the other track is the rhythm section only (rhythm section track). You should listen to the track with the soloist a few times before playing each etude to hear how it's performed. Listen for tone, time feel, phrasing, articulation, vibrato and musical interpretation. These elements of style can be quite subtle, so listen closely! Next play along with the soloist/rhythm section track, trying to match the soloist style.

After you've played along with the soloist/rhythm section track several times, go to the rhythm section only track and see if you can recreate the performance of the soloist. Remember, concentrate on style. You might even want to record yourself playing along with the rhythm section track and compare it to the soloist/rhythm section track. You can also practice the solos with just a metronome at different tempos.

To improvise during an etude, alternate between the etude and improvising. For example, play the first chorus, improvise on the second chorus until the last A section, then play the last A section out.

Für jede Etüde gibt es zwei Tracks. Auf einem Track ist der Solist mit der Rhythmusgruppe zu hören (Solist/Rhythm Section Track), auf dem anderen nur die Rhythmusgruppe (Rhythm Section Track). Hören Sie sich die Aufnahme mit dem Solisten einigemale an, bevor Sie eine Etüde spielen. Achten Sie dabei genau auf Tonbildung, Time Feel, Phrasierung, Artikulation, Vibrato und musikalische Interpretation. All diese stilistischen Elemente können sehr subtil wirken, hören Sie also genau zu. Spielen Sie nun mit dem Solisten und versuchen Sie, seinen Stil genau zu kopieren.

Versuchen Sie nun, nachdem Sie eine gewisse Zeit mit dem Solist/Rhythm Section Track geübt haben, nur zum Rhythm Section Track zu spielen und die Ausführung des Solisten genau wiederzugeben. Vergessen Sie nicht, genau auf die Stilistik zu achten. Sie können Ihr Spiel zudem zusammen mit der Rhythmusgruppe aufnehmen und mit der Ausführung des Solisten vergleichen, oder die Etüden nur mit dem Metronom in verschiedenen Tempi üben.

Verwenden Sie beim Improvisieren abwechselnd Material aus der Etüde und eigene Ideen. Spielen Sie zum Beispiel den ersten Chorus wie notiert, improvisieren Sie den zweiten Chorus und spielen Sie den letzten A–Teil wieder wie notiert.

Group Use for the Easy Jazz Conception Series

The Easy Jazz Conception Series is available for different instruments. Since the etudes are completely in unison and the phrasing is almost entirely the same between the different editions (alto sax, tenor sax., trumpet, trombone, guitar, etc.), the series can be useful in group instruction of jazz style.

Have the group listen to the soloist/rhythm section track from one of the books and follow along with the phrasing markings. Pay close attention to detail. Then have them play along with the soloist/rhythm section track, trying to match these style elements. Next, have them play along with the rhythm section track.

You can have different sections in a big band play different parts of the etude along with the rhythm section only track. For example:
Saxes – first two A sections
Trombones – bridge and last A section
Trumpets – first two A sections of the second chorus
Saxes, trombones and trumpets – bridge and last A section out

It's also possible to do this with soloists within a big band, or in a small group.

You can then have the horns play along with your rhythm section instead of the recording. Try to get the rhythm section to play with the same feeling as the rhythm section on the recording.

If you are using your rhythm section, it's possible to open up a section for improvisation. For example, open it up after the first chorus, having the rhythm section read the chords from the first chorus and repeat for solos. After the solos, have everyone come back in on the second chorus and take it out.

There are other possibilities too, so use your imagination (transposing up a half step, different tempos, feels, etc.)!

After you've mastered these etudes, try the more advanced etudes in the original **Jazz Conception Series.**

As stated in the original Jazz Conception Series, this is not meant as a replacement for listening to great jazz musicians like Louis Armstrong, Charlie Parker, Duke Ellington, Miles Davis, Count Basie, John Coltrane, Sonny Rollins, J.J. Johnson, Wes Montgomery, Thelonious Monk, Ray Brown, Dizzy Gillespie, and many more. It is meant as an introduction and a supplement to their music. It is really a tribute to them. I hope you find it both enjoyable and useful.

Jim Snidero

Easy Concepion Serie als Bandmethode

Die Easy Jazz Conception Reihe ist für verschiedene Instrumente erhältlich. Da die Melodien und Phrasierungen in den unterschiedlichen Ausgaben (Alt-, Tenorsaxophon, Trompete, Posaune, Gitarre, usw.) beinahe identisch sind, eignet sich die Reihe sehr gut für den Gruppenunterricht in Jazzstilistik.

Die ganze Gruppe sollte sich zuerst die Aufnahme mit dem Solisten anhören und anhand der jeweiligen Ausgabe genau die Phrasierungszeichen beachten. Hören Sie dabei genau auf die Nuancen. Lassen Sie anschließend die ganze Band zur Aufnahme mit dem Solisten spielen und arbeiten Sie an den stilistischen Elementen. Danach können Sie zusammen mit der Rhythmusgruppe, ohne Solist, spielen.

Lassen Sie die verschiedenen Sätze einer Big Band unterschiedliche Teile einer Etüde zum Rhythmusgruppen-Track spielen. Zum Beispiel:
Saxophone – die ersten zwei A–Teile
Posaunen – den Mittelteil und den letzten A–Teil
Trompeten – die ersten zwei A–Teile des zweiten Chorusses
Saxophone, Posaunen und Trompeten – den Mittelteil und den letzten A–Teil

Dieselben Aufteilungen können Sie mit den Solisten in einer Big Band oder Combo vornehmen.

Sie können die Bläser statt zur Aufnahme auch mit der eigenen Rhythmusgruppe spielen lassen. Diese sollte versuchen, mit dem gleichen Feeling, das die Rhythmusgruppe auf der Aufnahme vermittelt, zu spielen.

Wenn Sie mit Ihrer eigenen Rhythmusgruppe arbeiten, können Sie die Form offener gestalten und Raum für Improvisationen lassen. Die Rhythmusgruppe kann zum Beispiel nach dem ersten Chorus die Harmonien wiederholen während über diese Form improvisiert wird. Nach den Soli steigt die Band wieder mit dem zweiten Chorus ein und spielt bis zum Schluss.

Es gibt viele andere Möglichkeiten der Gestaltung, Ihrer Vorstellungskraft sind keine Grenzen gesetzt (einen Halbtonschritt nach oben transponieren, unterschiedliche Tempi, Feels, usw.)

Wenn Sie diese Etüden gemeistert haben, können Sie sich mit den fortgeschrittenen Etüden der originalen **Jazz Conception Serie** beschäftigen.

Wie ich bereits in der Jazz Conception Serie gesagt habe, kann diese Reihe nicht das Hören der Musik großer Jazzmusiker wie Louis Armstrong, Charlie Parker, Duke Ellington, Miles Davis, Count Basie, John Coltrane, Sonny Rollins, J.J. Johnson, Wes Montgomery, Thelonious Monk, Ray Brown, Dizzy Gillespie und vieler anderer ersetzen. Sie versteht sich als eine Einführung in ihre Musik, eine Ergänzung und als Zeichen der Wertschätzung. Ich hoffe, Sie haben Spaß und Nutzen von dieser Reihe.

Jim Snidero

Basie's Blues

Track 1/18

Jim Snidero

Morning Calm

Jim Snidero

So Long Birdie

Jim Snidero

Feb 2023

Bye Bye Blackbird.

82 bars song

D maj 2nd tune

Hot and Humid

Jim Snidero

Rock On

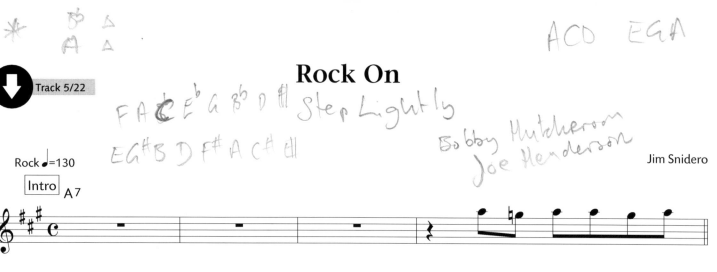

Important Events

Milestones

Jim Snidero

♩=165

Chorus 1

Shufflin' in F

Jim Snidero

Bossa at Night

Duke's Convoy

Caravan

Jim Snidero

Latin ♩= 82

A 13♭9♯11

D–6   Eø   A 7 alt.   E/D–7

Swing

D 7

G 7

C 7

Mist and Grits

Jim Snidero

Caliente Blues

Prince Charming

Jim Snidero

Bird's Backyard

Jim Snidero

Us

Jim Snidero

x = False fingering. Finger low C with octave key.
o = Normal fingering.

Love is Easy

ABOUT THE COMPOSER

Jim Snidero studied at the University of North Texas, then moved to New York City in 1981. He has recorded as a leader for Toshiba/EMI, Criss-Cross, Double-Time, and Red Records, among others. He has been a member of Toshiko Akiyoshi's Jazz Orchestra for over ten years, performed and recorded with Frank Sinatra, Jack McDuff, Eddie Palmieri and Frank Wess, among others, and is a frequent member of the Mingus Big Band. Snidero is also an instructor at the Mannes School of Music in New York City. He has given jazz workshops throughout the U.S., Europe and Japan, and is a Selmer clinician.

Jim Snidero studierte an der University of North Texas. 1981 zog er nach New York. Als Bandleader hat er für Toshiba/EMI, Criss-Cross, Double-Time und Red Records aufgenommen. Seit mehr als zehn Jahren ist er Mitglied des Toshiko Akiyoshi Jazz Orchesters, spielte u.a. in den Bands von Frank Sinatra, Jack McDuff, Eddie Palmieri und Frank Wess, mit denen er auch Aufnahmen machte. Er spielt außerdem regelmäßig mit der Mingus Big Band. Als Lehrer ist er an der New School in New York City tätig. Er gab zudem Kurse an vielen Schulen in den U.S.A., in Europa und in Japan. Jim Snidero spielt Selmer Saxophone.

The Jazz Conception Series
by Jim Snidero

The Jazz Conception Series is the best-selling and most widely used jazz etude material in the world. Each book has between 15-21 etudes and online audio tracks that will help you to sound both authentic and convincing when playing jazz.

Used in countless schools around the world, these etudes have provided students, teachers and even professional musicians with deeply authentic compositions that have helped them to become better jazz musicians and improvisers.

Additionally, the Intermediate Jazz Conception and the Jazz Conception series' numerous melodic examples and vocabulary studies are of great help to get you going on your musician journey.

Available for all major jazz instruments

Historically-significant artists

Highest production quality

MA 9028-02 11/18

The *Easy* Jazz Conception Series

Alto Sax ADV 14760	**Trombone** ADV 14763	**Cello** ADV 14772
Tenor & Soprano Sax ADV 14761	**Flute** ADV 14764	**Guitar** ADV 14766
Baritone Sax ADV 14773	**Clarinet** ADV 14765	**Bass Lines** ADV 1468
The Sax Section ADV 14774	**Violin** ADV 14770	**Piano comping** ADV 14767
Trumpet ADV 14762	**Viola** ADV 14771	**Drums** ADV 14769

The Jazz Conception Series

Alto & Baritone Sax ADV 14720	**Flute** ADV 14724	**Bass lines** ADV 14736
Tenor & Soprano Sax ADV 14721	**Clarinet** ADV 14725	**Drums** ADV 14729
The Sax Section ADV 14731	**Piano** ADV 14727	**Scat Vocal** ADV 14737
Trumpet ADV 14722	**Piano comping** ADV 14739	**Study Guide (E)** ADV 14730
Trombone ADV 14723	**Guitar** ADV 14726	**Handbuch (D)** ADV 14738
Bass Trombone ADV 14735	**Bass** ADV 14728	

The *Intermediate* Jazz Conception Series

Alto & Baritone Sax ADV 14780	**Flute** ADV 14784	**Bass** ADV 14788
Tenor & Soprano Sax ADV 14781	**Clarinet** ADV 14785	**Drums** ADV 14789
Trumpet ADV 14782	**Piano** ADV 14787	
Trombone ADV 14783	**Guitar** ADV 14786	

www.advancemusic.com